ALL ABOUT DOG

A GREAT PLACE TO RECORD, STORE AND MANAGE ALL THE DETAILS OF YOUR PET'S LIFE

Parragon

Bath • New York • Singapore • Hong Kong • Cologne • Delhi
Melbourne • Amsterdam • Johannesburg • Auckland • Shenzhen

This edition published by Parragon in 2012

Parragon
Queen Street House
4 Queen Street
Bath BA1 1HE, UK
www.parragon.com

ISBN 978-1-4454-3514-5

Printed in China

Created and produced by Ivy Contract

Front cover image: jack russell puppy © Steve Shott/Getty Images
Back cover images: spaniel © Parragon Books Ltd; labrador puppies and golden retriever puppy © istockphoto
Page four image: © Rich Johnson/Fotolia

A note about the recipes

All the recipes in this book have been carefully put together with advice from veterinary surgeons and tried out on different dogs. However it is not impossible that in individual cases some meals may have negative consequences. The publishers and author can accept no liability for such consequences.

Not everything that human beings like to consume is good for dogs. Indisputably harmful are alcohol, cocoa, garlic, raisins, the onion family, chocolate with a high proportion of cocoa butter, raw pork and hot spicy dishes. A few studies and internet pages classify further foodstuffs as poorly tolerated by dogs. Other sources – the veterinary surgeons we consulted among them – disagree with these opinions.

If you are uncertain in any way about how well your dog will tolerate certain ingredients, you should consult your veterinary surgeon.

A note about safety during training

Due to some breeds' body shapes, some dogs may find it difficult to balance in various positions. If your dog is pregnant, old or has any health conditions, check with your vet before you start training.

All About Your Dog

You love your dog. And they love you right back with unconditional adoration. Other people have dogs, of course, and although they are lovely too, they are not as all-round smart, gorgeous and lovable as yours. So celebrate your dog with this interactive book: more than just a place to keep all your pooch's paperwork or a photo album, it's a permanent doggie journal of the good times (the first car trip, ears streaming in the wind) and the not-so-good (that ineradicable stain on the carpet). It's a chance to chart your pet's progress, from puppyhood to confident, indispensable pet.

'Happiness is dog-shaped, I say.'
CHAPMAN PINCHER

Doggie Stats

Name:

DOB:

Place of birth:

Breed/combination of breeds:

Gender:

Eye colour:

Fur length:

Coat colour and markings:

Distinctive features:

Parents' names:

Number of puppies in the litter:

Previous owner's/breeder's name:

Contact details:

'Scratch a dog and you'll find a friend for life.'
FRANKLIN P. JONES

I chose

... as my dog's name because ...

Just Look At My Dog

Meet The Family

Firsts

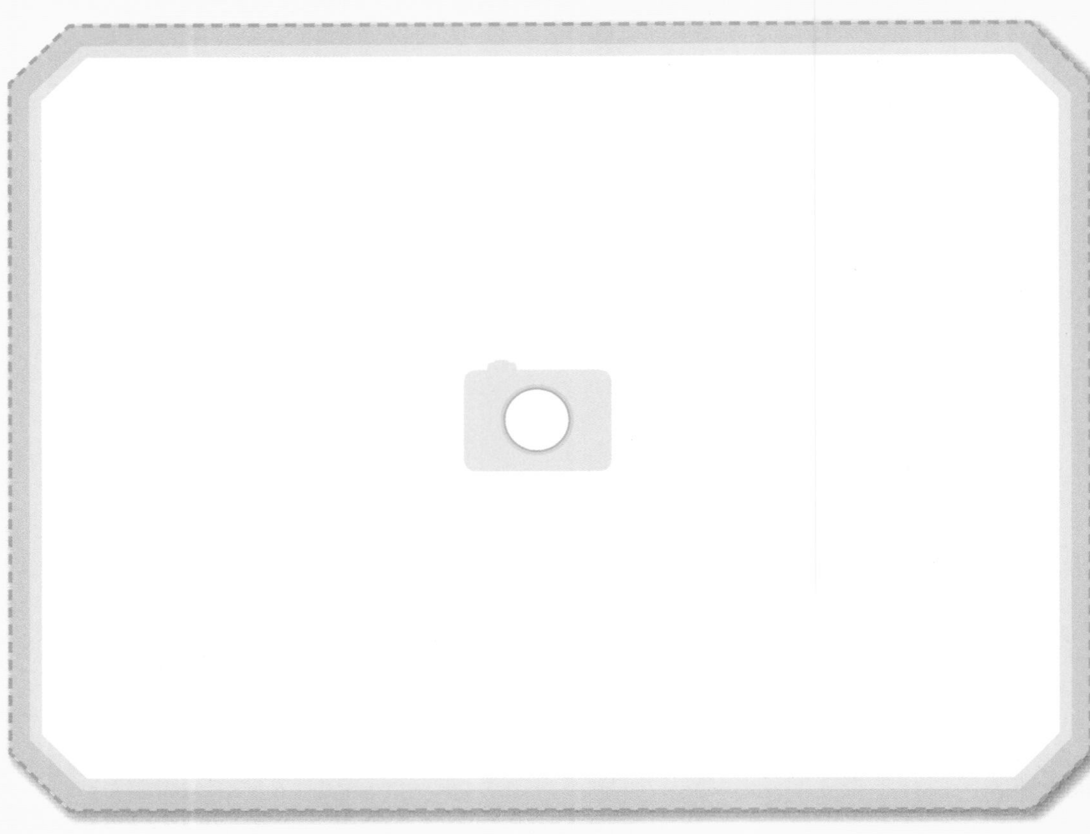

First day in new home

Date

Notes

First walk

Date

Notes

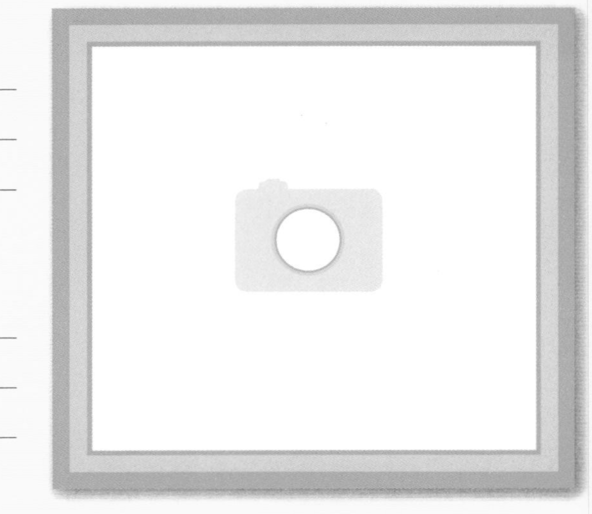

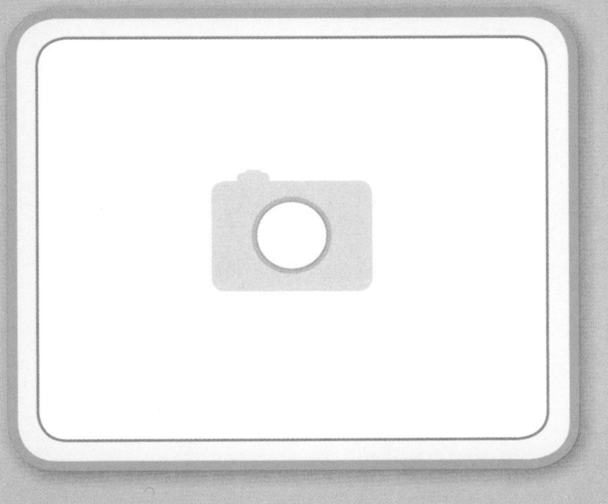

First car ride

Date

Notes

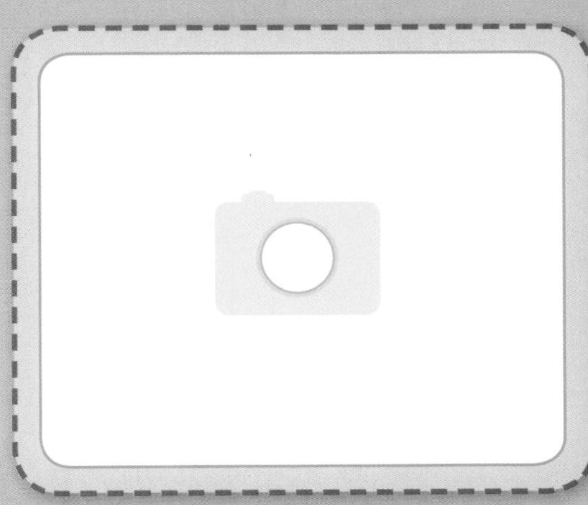

First trip/holiday/visit

Date

Notes

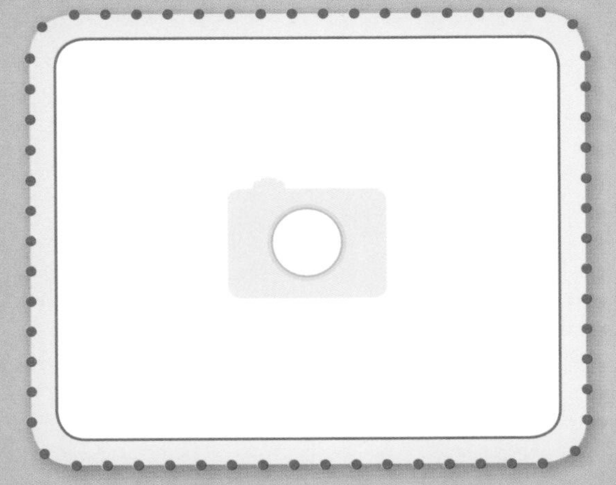

First birthday

Date

Notes

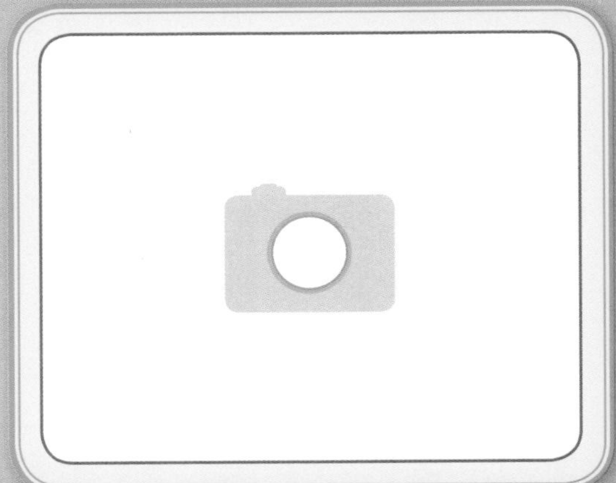

First toy

Date

Notes

What A Personality!

My dog is:

- [ ] Friendly
- [ ] Eager to please
- [ ] Playful
- [ ] Nervous/Anxious
- [ ] Bossy
- [ ] Stubborn
- [ ] Aggressive
- [ ] Shy/Timid
- [ ] Unpredictable
- [ ] Crazy
- [ ] Easily frightened
- [ ] Good with children
- [ ] Good with other dogs
- [ ] Good with other pets

Tick Box

The best thing about

____

is ______________________________

____

____

____

I wish

____

wouldn't ______________________________

____

____

____

____

I love my dog because ...

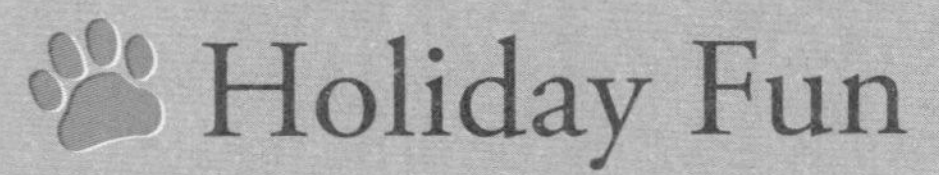

Holiday Fun

As part of the family, why wouldn't you want to take your dog on holiday with you? Sometimes it just won't work; it's too stressful for the dog or just too expensive (so maybe long-haul to a Kenyan safari park is out). But, with a bit of organization and planning, it will be fine. Just make sure you have all the paperwork to hand and the jabs are up-to-date. Try touring in a motorhome, or camping if you are made of hardier stuff; if not, there are plenty of listings of dog-friendly places to stay, so there's no need to leave your best friend behind while you go off to have fun.

Remember to take:

- [ ] Dog bed
- [ ] Pet insurance document
- [ ] Favourite toys
- [ ] Favourite treats
- [ ] Lead
- [ ] Poop scoop
- [ ] Record of microchip number
- [ ] Travel water bowl and food

Tick Box

Holiday memories

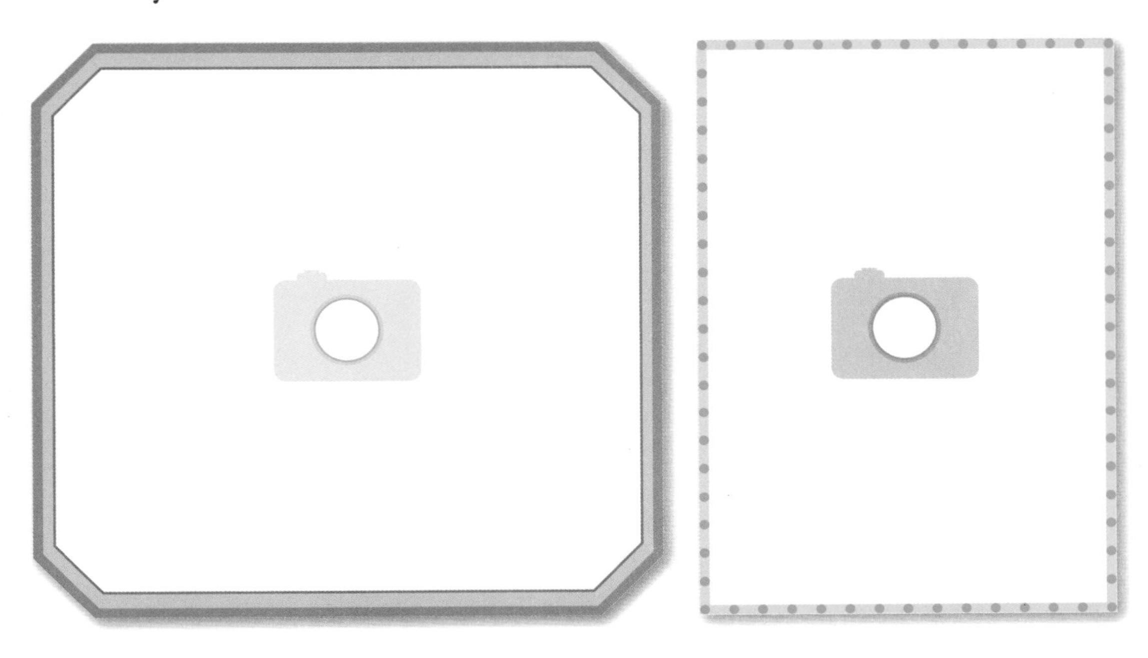

When

Where

Made friends with

When

Where

Had a crush on

Holiday memories

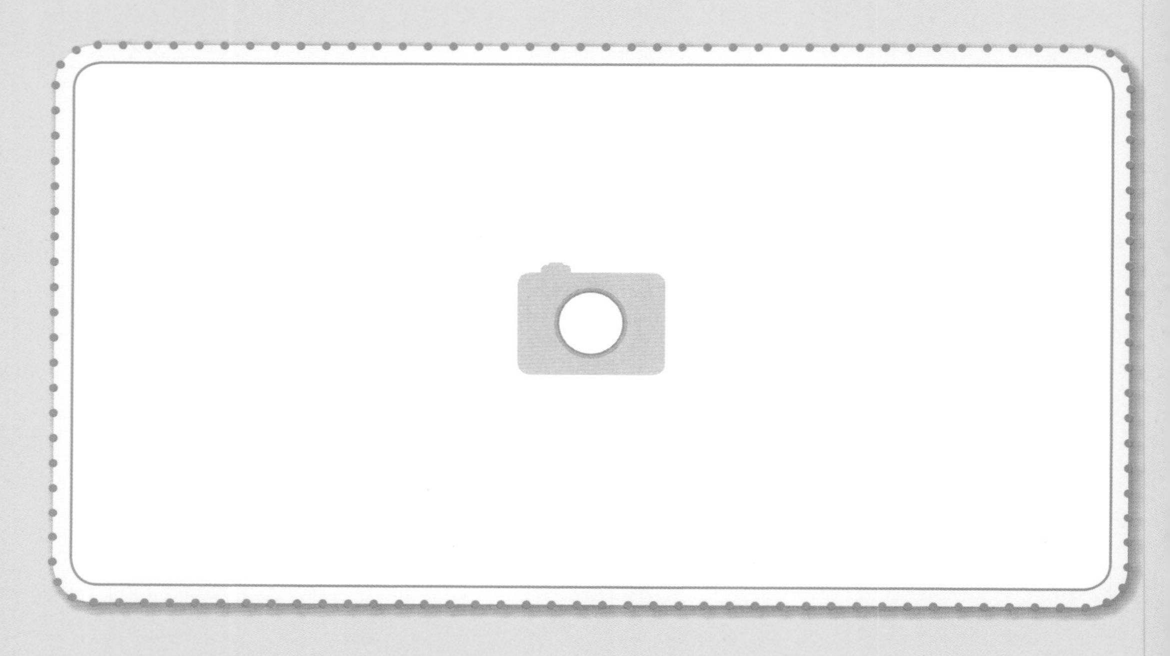

When

Where

Made us laugh because

When

Where

Embarrassed us because

Grooming

Hands up all those who have enough dog hair under the sofa to knit another dog? It goes with the territory, especially in spring when the winter coat is shed. Don't panic! There are ways to minimize the hairstorm; get your dog used to daily grooming from puppyhood, and if you have a longhair, book in regular salon trimming sessions. And most dogs adore a bath – every two or three months is enough.

The trials and tribulations ...

Grooming check

Type of coat	Brushing needs
☐ long	☐ little brushing
☐ short	☐ twice a week
☐ curly	☐ clipping

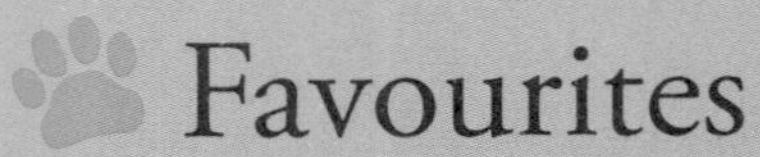

Favourites

Favourite toys

Favourite walks

Favourite games

Favourite sleeping places

Favourite places to be petted

Favourite foods

Favourite exercise

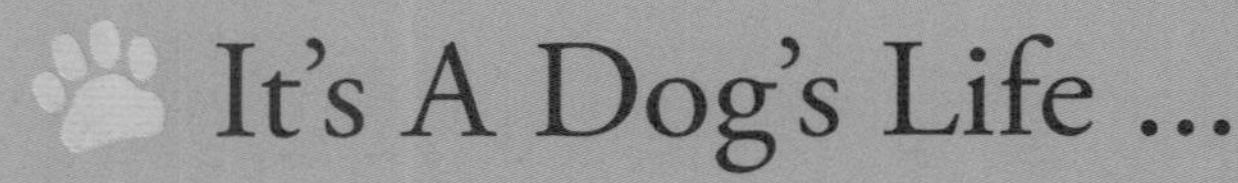

It's A Dog's Life ...

Pen a poem or stick in those cherished photos. Here is where you can celebrate your canine companion in any way you choose.

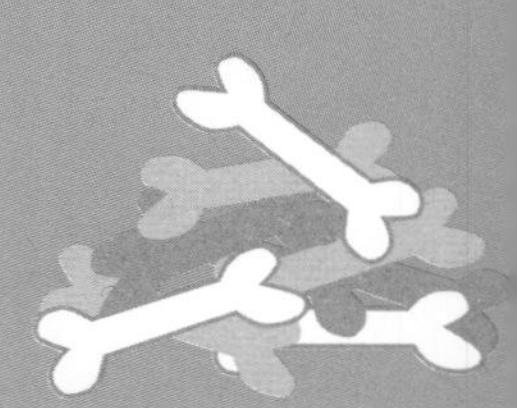

It's a dog's life ...

It’s a dog’s life …

It's a dog's life …

It's a dog's life …

Training: The Basics

How to be a good trainer

Just like us, dogs learn by understanding that how they behave has consequences; training is all about making the consequences rewarding, and the behaviour worth repeating. Carrot, not stick, see?

Always reward with treats, praise and lots of love when your dog does what is required. Any naughty behaviour needs to be ignored.

Some dogs respond well to a clicker, in addition to treats, strokes and praise. Use it when your dog does what you want, clicking to announce the arrival of a treat. Pretty soon, the clicking becomes a reward in itself by letting your dog know that he or she is getting it right.

Keep it short and sweet, little and often; if your dog doesn't enjoy the training, it won't work.

TRICK TIPS

- Start training early in your dog's life
- Plan your training session
- Always use treats and toys to motivate your dog
- Practise and perfect your timing
- Be consistent
- Always have water available
- Stay patient
- Keep training sessions fun
- Make it clear when a session is over
- Always end on a good note

'No matter how little money and how few possessions you own, having a dog makes you rich.'

LOUIS SABIN

Sitting Pretty

'Sit' is really useful, and if you don't do anything else, get this one down. It will stop bouncier breeds jumping up at people, and keep your dog under control when crossing the road. Practise 'sit' in different places; no use having a dog that can sit at home but runs riot in the park!

1 Hold a treat in front of your dog's nose and raise it above their head.

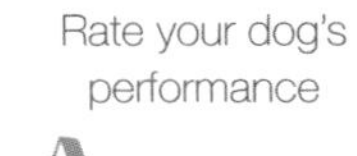

Rate your dog's performance

Gold

Silver

Bronze

2 As the head goes up to follow the treat, the bottom should sink down. Don't be tempted to push it down and do the trick for your dog – just wait it out, giving plenty of praise.

'SIT!'

3 When your dog is sitting, give the treat and lavish more praise. Try it some more, then say 'sit' just before their bottom hits the floor.

TOP TIP

Once you've mastered this trick, hold your hand out flat without a treat, then raise it towards your shoulder to lure your dog into the sit position. He or she will start to learn the hand signal for 'sit', and you won't have to rely on treats!

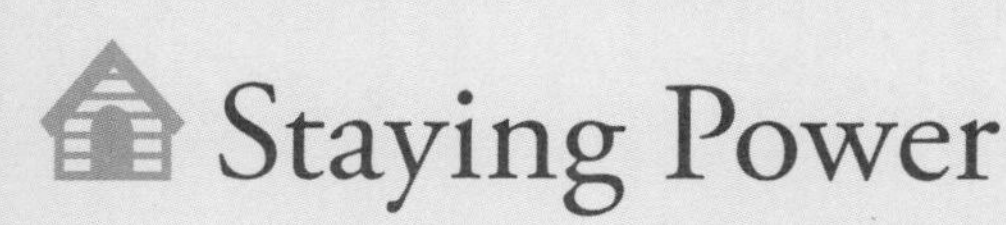

Staying Power

If you and your dog can get 'sit' nailed, then 'stay' will be a shoo-in, since it is really just 'sit', with an added hand gesture. The aim is to get your dog to sit still until asked to move. Keep practising and you will have the best-trained dog in the park!

1 Ask your dog to 'sit'. Now, teach the hand signal for stay; extend your hand, palm up facing your dog, keep eye contact, and step back a little.

2 Keeping your palm flat, wait a second or so, then say 'stay', and move towards your dog. If the dog 'stays', reward with treats and love.

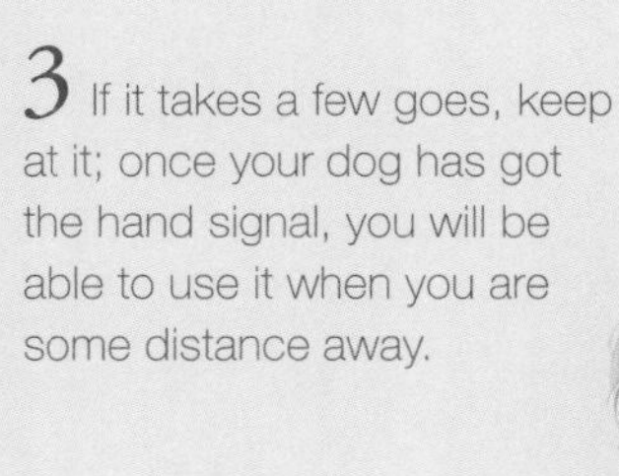

TOP TIP

Slowly build up the distance from your dog and also the time delay between saying 'stay' and returning to your dog. If you rush, your dog may ignore your command, undoing all your hard work.

Rate your dog's performance

 Gold

 Silver

 Bronze

3 If it takes a few goes, keep at it; once your dog has got the hand signal, you will be able to use it when you are some distance away.

Down!

Once you've both got 'sit' and 'stay' right, why not try 'down'? This will be a great help when you are having a quiet time in the pub or café, or to calm your dog when new people come to visit.

1 From the 'sit' position, get your dog's attention by holding out a treat in front of you. Make sure you choose a really tasty treat, as you are going to ask your dog to follow this morsel to the floor.

Rate your dog's performance

☆ Gold

☆ Silver

☆ Bronze

2 Don't panic if they don't get all the way down; wait, with your hand holding the treat on the floor; give the treat when the dog is lying down.

'DOWN!'

3 As with 'sit', practise a few times, then add the word 'down' as your dog hits the floor, before giving praise and a treat. When you think they have got the idea, delay the treat a bit. This way you'll show that this is a longhaul trick.

 Come On Over

Like the 'sit' command, you'll find 'come' essential, to get your dog back when they really want to jump in that duckpond/sandpit/traffic jam. It's never too early to start with this one, and you can expect a lifetime of refresher courses, as your dog learns to come to you, however tempting the distraction.

Rate your dog's performance

 Gold

 Silver

 Bronze

TOP TIP

Tone of voice and body language is key to achieving this command – be firm and consistent.

1 Choose a quiet place, make a fuss of your dog to get their attention, show that you have a treat in your hand, then gradually move away. Your dog should follow (don't flatter yourself, it's the treat, not you).

2 Say 'come' and your dog's name; as your dog approaches, hand over the treat with lots of praise and love. You will suddenly be a very attractive object indeed.

Drop It, Leave It

There are many things you'd rather your dog didn't pick up (some of them very eeuuch) so it makes sense to teach them to 'drop it' on command. You will have to seize the time with this one, catching your dog chomping on a not-so-favourite toy.

Rate your dog's performance

Gold

Silver

Bronze

1 When you see your dog carrying a toy, get ready with your treat, and offer it.

2 The treat should tempt your dog to drop the toy in exchange (unless it is a truly beloved favourite). Pick up the toy, hand over the treat and heap on the praise.

3 Once your dog has the idea, say 'drop it' and point to the ground. Always have a treat ready; no-one wants to give up something for nothing.

Go Fetch!

Fetch is really fun for both of you, and does all that doggy-human bonding thing effortlessly as well as turning a walk into an event. Don't despair if your pooch does not pick up this game as quickly as a labrador or a spaniel – they are professional fetchers.

TOP TIP

Dog not interested in toys? Try food! First, give your dog a treat for just a sniff of the toy. Next, wait for your dog to put its mouth around a toy before offering a treat. He'll soon pick up anything in return for a treat!

1 Start off gently indoors, teasing your dog by moving a favourite toy around and leaving it out of reach. When your dog goes to get it, treat and praise.

'FETCH!'

'DROP!'

Rate your dog's performance

 Gold

 Silver

 Bronze

2 Throw the toy further away and urge your dog to 'fetch'. Give more treats and praise if successful.

3 Teach your dog to 'drop it', if you haven't already, so that you can throw the toy again when it is brought back. When you take the trick outdoors, it will help keep you fit as well as your dog.

Trick Score Sheet

Trick name	Date started	Date mastered	Rating 1–5
Sitting Pretty			
Staying Power			
Get Down On It			
Come On Over			
Drop It, Leave It			
Go Fetch!			

Favourite trick: ______________________

Struggles with: ______________________

All about training my dog

Now after the tricks, come the treats. On the following pages, you'll find six recipes for tasty titbits for your pet.

Banana Biscuits

Ingredients

2 carrots, finely grated

1 banana, mashed

200 g (7 oz) all-purpose flour

100 g (3 oz) fine rolled oats

50 ml (1 fl oz) sunflower oil

water as required

Makes about 30 biscuits

Method

1 Mix the carrots, banana, flour, rolled oats and oil together to make a dough, adding a little water if necessary.

2 Preheat the oven to 180°C (350°F). Line a baking sheet with baking parchment. Roll out the dough to about 1 cm (½ inch) thick and cut into 4 cm (1½ inches) squares.

3 Bake for 25 minutes and let cool overnight in the turned-off oven. Store in a paper or linen bag. The biscuits will keep for about 3 weeks.

First tried ______________

____

Loved ______________ ☐

Quite liked ______________ ☐

Not at all impressed ______ ☐

 Buttermilk Snacks

Ingredients

250 g (9 oz) chicken livers

1 tablespoon sunflower oil

100 ml (3 fl oz) buttermilk

250 g (9 oz) wholegrain flour

Makes about 35 snacks

Method

1 Chop the livers, and mix with the sunflower oil and buttermilk, then add the flour. Knead together to make a smooth dough. Cover, and let rest in the fridge for 30 minutes.

2 Roll out the dough to about 1 cm (½ inch) thick. Cut out bone shapes with a cookie cutter or a sharp knife.

3 Bake the snacks at 180°C (350°F) (with fan) for 30 minutes on a baking sheet. Turn off the oven and let the biscuits dry in the oven for another hour. Store in a biscuit tin for up to 2 weeks.

First tried ______________

____

Loved ______________ ☐

Quite liked ______________ ☐

Not at all impressed ______________ ☐

TOP TIP

Chicken livers are, in moderation, a great source of nutrition for your dog. They are rich in protein – essential for your dog's growth and energy – and vitamin A. For a change, try substituting lamb livers for the chicken livers.

Reward Biscuits

Ingredients

100 g (3½ oz) wholewheat flour
100 g (3½ oz) coarse rolled oats
2 tablespoons oat bran
2 eggs, lightly beaten
75 g (2½ oz) grated Parmesan cheese
75 g (2½ oz) finely diced ham
100 ml (3 fl oz) water

Makes about 35 biscuits

Method

1 Mix all the ingredients with the water to make a smooth dough. Cover and let the dough rest for about 30 minutes.

2 Preheat the oven to 180°C (350°F). Line a baking sheet with baking parchment.

3 Roll out the dough to about 1 cm (½ inch) thick and cut into 3 cm x 5 cm (1 inch x 2 inch) rectangles. Bake for 25 minutes. Turn off the heat and let the biscuits harden in the oven for another 2 hours. Store in a paper or linen bag. The biscuits will keep for about 4 weeks.

First tried ______________

____

Loved ______________ ☐

Quite liked ______________ ☐

Not at all impressed ______________ ☐

TOP TIP

If you're making a batch of biscuits to use as rewards, keep each biscuit small; that way your dog can be given a lot of rewards without getting full.

Cheese Crunchies

Ingredients

100 g (3½ oz) chopped almonds

100 g (3½ oz) roughly chopped hazelnuts

150 g (5 oz) grated Emmental cheese

4 eggs, lightly beaten

550 g (1 lb 3 oz) buckwheat flour

1 tablespoon honey

water and flour as required

Makes about 30 crunchies

Method

1 Toast the almonds and hazelnuts in a non-stick pan, without oil or fat, until a light brown. Remove from the heat and let them cool.

2 Knead all the ingredients into a smooth dough, adding a little more water or flour as necessary.

3 Preheat the oven to 160°C (325°F). Line a baking sheet with baking parchment.

4 Roll out the dough to about 1 cm (½ inch) thick. Cut into 2 cm x 5 cm (1 inch x 2 inches) rectangles.

5 Place the biscuits on the baking sheet. Bake for 1 hour. Turn off the heat and let the biscuits dry for another hour in the oven. Store in a paper or linen bag; they will keep for about 4 weeks.

First tried ______________

____

Loved ______________ ☐

Quite liked ______________ ☐

Not at all impressed ______________ ☐

Tuna Triangles

TOP TIP
For an extra special treat, sprinkle grated cheese, such as Parmesan or Cheddar, over the top of the triangles before baking.

First tried ______________________

____

Loved ______________ ☐

Quite liked ______________ ☐

Not at all impressed ________ ☐

Method

1 Whizz the drained tuna, oil and egg in a blender, then mix with the other ingredients to make a dough.

2 Preheat the oven to 180°C (350°F). Line a baking sheet with baking parchment.

3 Roll out the dough to about 1 cm (½ inch) thick and cut it into triangles. Place the biscuits on the baking sheet and bake for 25 minutes. Store in a biscuit tin for up to 2 weeks.

Ingredients

1 can tuna fish in spring water, drained

4 tablespoons extra virgin olive oil

1 egg

1 teaspoon dried thyme

1 teaspoon dried oregano

250 g (9 oz) cornflour

150 g (5 oz) rolled oats

50 g (2 oz) flour

Makes about 40 triangles

Crispy Bacon Rolls

Ingredients

150 g (5 oz) wholewheat flour
150 g (5 oz) wholegrain rye flour
75 g (2½ oz) wheat grains
75 g (2½ oz) bacon cubes
1 tablespoon brewer's yeast
3 tablespoons sunflower oil
250 ml (8½ fl oz) unsalted meat stock
75 g (2½ oz) cracked bulgur wheat

Makes about 30 rolls

First tried ________________

Loved __________ ☐

Quite liked __________ ☐

Not at all impressed __________ ☐

Method

1 Mix all the ingredients, except for the bulgur wheat, into a dough. Cover, and let rest for 30 minutes.

2 Preheat the oven to 180°C (350°F). Line a baking sheet with baking parchment.

3 Shape large spoonfuls of the dough into balls and roll them in the bulgur wheat. Bake for 45 minutes, then turn off the heat, and let dry in the oven until quite hard. Store in a paper or linen bag for about 3 weeks.

Doggie Delights

There's room on the next few pages for you to write up your dog's favourite recipes, and even note their favourite shop-bought pet food. If you create your own recipes please consult your vet for the most recent list of ingredients that should not be given to a dog.

Favourite shop-bought pet food:

Really doesn't like:

enjoying their favourite dinner

My recipes

My recipes

Routine Health

Keep a record of vaccinations, boosters and other healthcare routines all in one place to help keep your dog in tip-top condition.

TOP TIP If you choose to microchip your dog, remember to update your details with the microchipping company if you move house or change your contact details.

Microchip number ______________________

Date microchipped ______________________

Date neutered/spayed ______________________

Vaccinations

Type	Date

Boosters

Type	Date

Dental check-ups

Date and time ______ Date and time ______
Date and time ______ Date and time ______
Date and time ______ Date and time ______
Date and time ______ Date and time ______
Date and time ______ Date and time ______
Date and time ______ Date and time ______
Date and time ______ Date and time ______
Date and time ______ Date and time ______
Date and time ______ Date and time ______
Date and time ______ Date and time ______
Date and time ______ Date and time ______

Flea treatments

Date given ______ Date given ______
Date given ______ Date given ______
Date given ______ Date given ______
Date given ______ Date given ______
Date given ______ Date given ______
Date given ______ Date given ______
Date given ______ Date given ______
Date given ______ Date given ______
Date given ______ Date given ______
Date given ______ Date given ______
Date given ______ Date given ______

Worming

Date given
Date given
Date given
Date given
Date given
Date given
Date given
Date given
Date given
Date given
Date given
Date given
Date given
Date given
Date given
Date given
Date given
Date given
Date given

Date given
Date given
Date given
Date given
Date given
Date given
Date given
Date given
Date given
Date given
Date given
Date given
Date given
Date given
Date given
Date given
Date given
Date given
Date given

Date given
Date given
Date given
Date given
Date given
Date given

TOP TIP

It's not always easy to tell if your dog is infested with worms as often there aren't any symptoms of ill health. Prevention is better than cure, and vets recommend that dogs are wormed at least every three months.

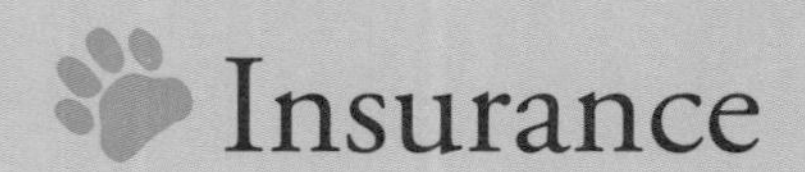

Insurance

Insurance company details

Contact name: ______________________

Address: ______________________

____

____

Phone: ______________________

Email: ______________________

Policy number: ______________________

Policy renewal date: ______________________

Deductables/excess and exclusions: ______________________

____

____

____

____

____

____

____

____

'If you are a dog and your owner suggests that you wear a sweater ... suggest that he wear a tail.'

FRAN LEBOWITZ

TOP TIP

Be clear about what your insurance policy covers. For example, if your dog has a pre-existing health condition, any illness relating to this may not be covered by your insurance.

Health Record

Health conditions and allergies

Medication and nutritional supplements

Date

Medication or supplement

Dosage/instructions

Date

Medication or supplement

Dosage/instructions

Date

Medication or supplement

Dosage/instructions

Date

Medication or supplement

Dosage/instructions

Medication and nutritional supplements

Date

Medication or supplement

Dosage/instructions

Date

Medication or supplement

Dosage/instructions

Date

Medication or supplement

Dosage/instructions

Date

Medication or supplement

Dosage/instructions

Visits to the vet

Date

Age

Details of illness, test or treatment

Date

Age

Details of illness, test or treatment

Date

Age

Details of illness, test or treatment

Date

Age

Details of illness, test or treatment

Visits to the vet

Date

Age

Details of illness, test or treatment

Date

Age

Details of illness, test or treatment

Date

Age

Details of illness, test or treatment

Date

Age

Details of illness, test or treatment

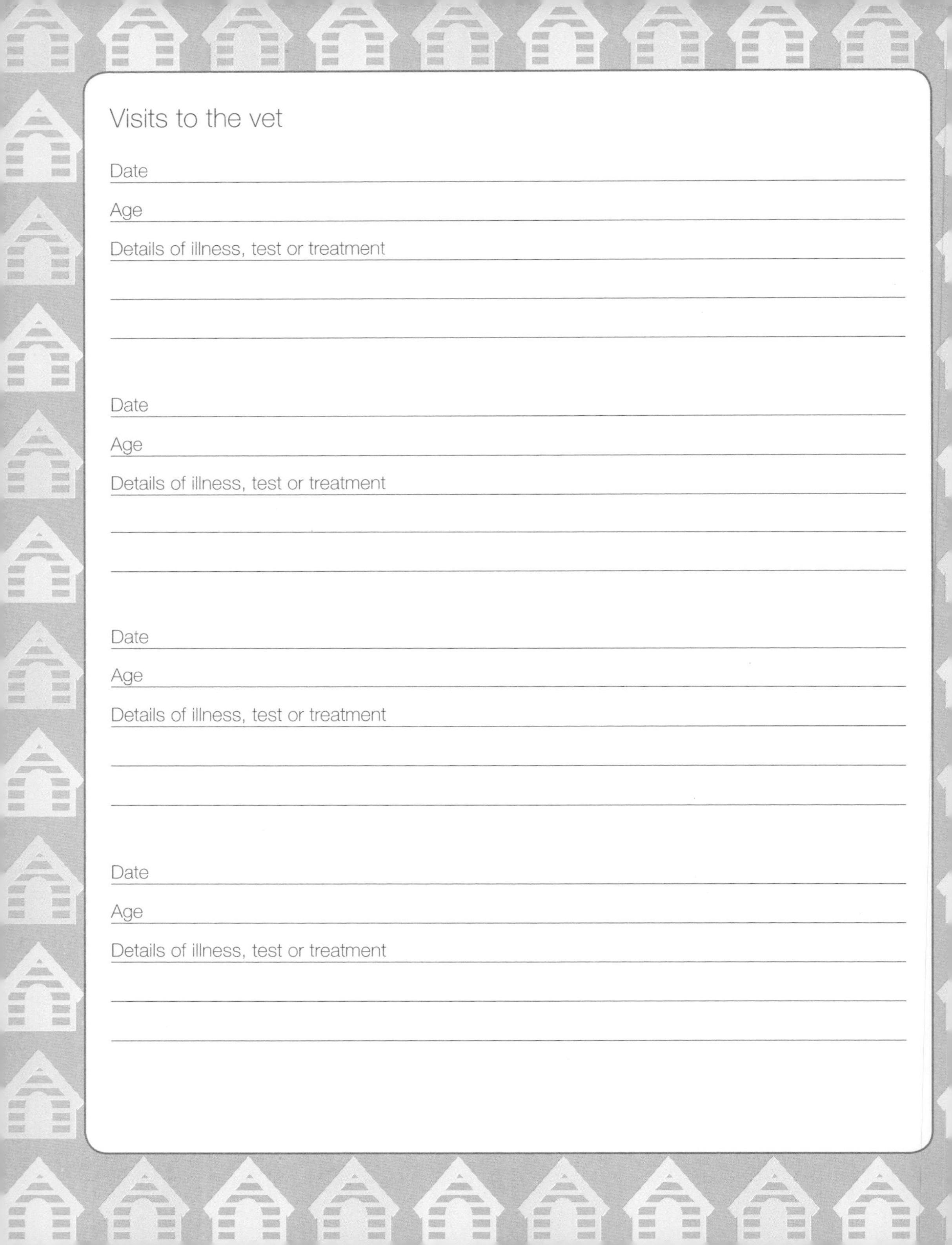

Visits to the vet

Date

Age

Details of illness, test or treatment

Date

Age

Details of illness, test or treatment

Date

Age

Details of illness, test or treatment

Date

Age

Details of illness, test or treatment

Year-To-View Health Calendar

January

February

May

June

September

October

March

April

July

August

November

December

Year-To-View Health Calendar

January

February

May

June

September

October

March

April

July

August

November

December

Doggie Contacts

Vet

Contact name

Address

Phone Email

Animal hospital

Contact name

Address

Phone Email

Insurance company

Contact name

Address

Phone Email

Boarding for your dog

Contact name

Address

Phone Email

Dog sitter

Name

Address

Phone Email

Dog walker

Name

Address

Phone Email

Grooming parlour

Name

Address

Phone Email

Further addresses

Name

Address

Phone Email

Further addresses

Name

Address

Phone

Email

Further addresses

Name

Address

Phone

Email

Further addresses

Name

Address

Phone

Email

Further addresses

Name

Address

Phone

Email

Further addresses

Name

Address

Phone Email

Further addresses

Name

Address

Phone Email

Further addresses

Name

Address

Phone Email

Further addresses

Name

Address

Phone Email

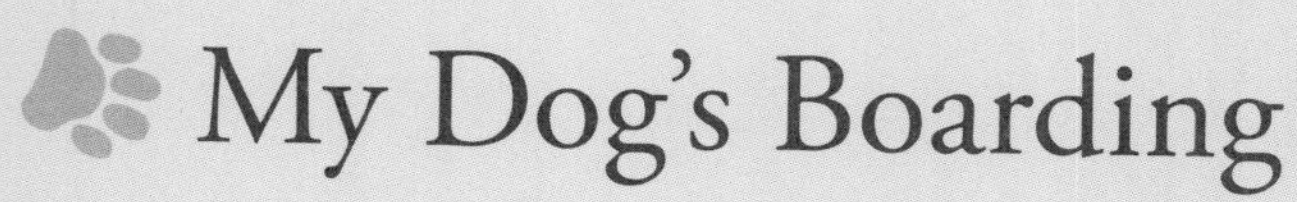

My Dog's Boarding

Sometimes you just won't be able to take your dog on holiday, or there may be an emergency, and you will have to use boarding kennels, or get a dog sitter (often a good choice if your dog is venerably ancient). Talk to your vet and doggy friends before choosing kennels, and don't be afraid to go and visit before committing – you need to see for yourself how the dogs are kept and if the regime fits your dog's personality and preferences. Don't worry, your dog won't forget you, and you will be greeted like a returning hero when you collect them.

Remember:
Pet's vaccination certificate
Your contact details
Medication
Favourite toy

Before you go, make sure:

- ☐ Vaccinations are up to date, including kennel cough vaccination
- ☐ You book your pet in early, to save last-minute panic
- ☐ You inform the boarding facility of any allergies or special dietary needs

Tick Box

Notes

____

____

____

____

____

____

____

____

Paws for thought ...

Space for memories, pictures, doggie doodles and more.

Paws for thought ...

Paws for thought ...

Doggie
photos

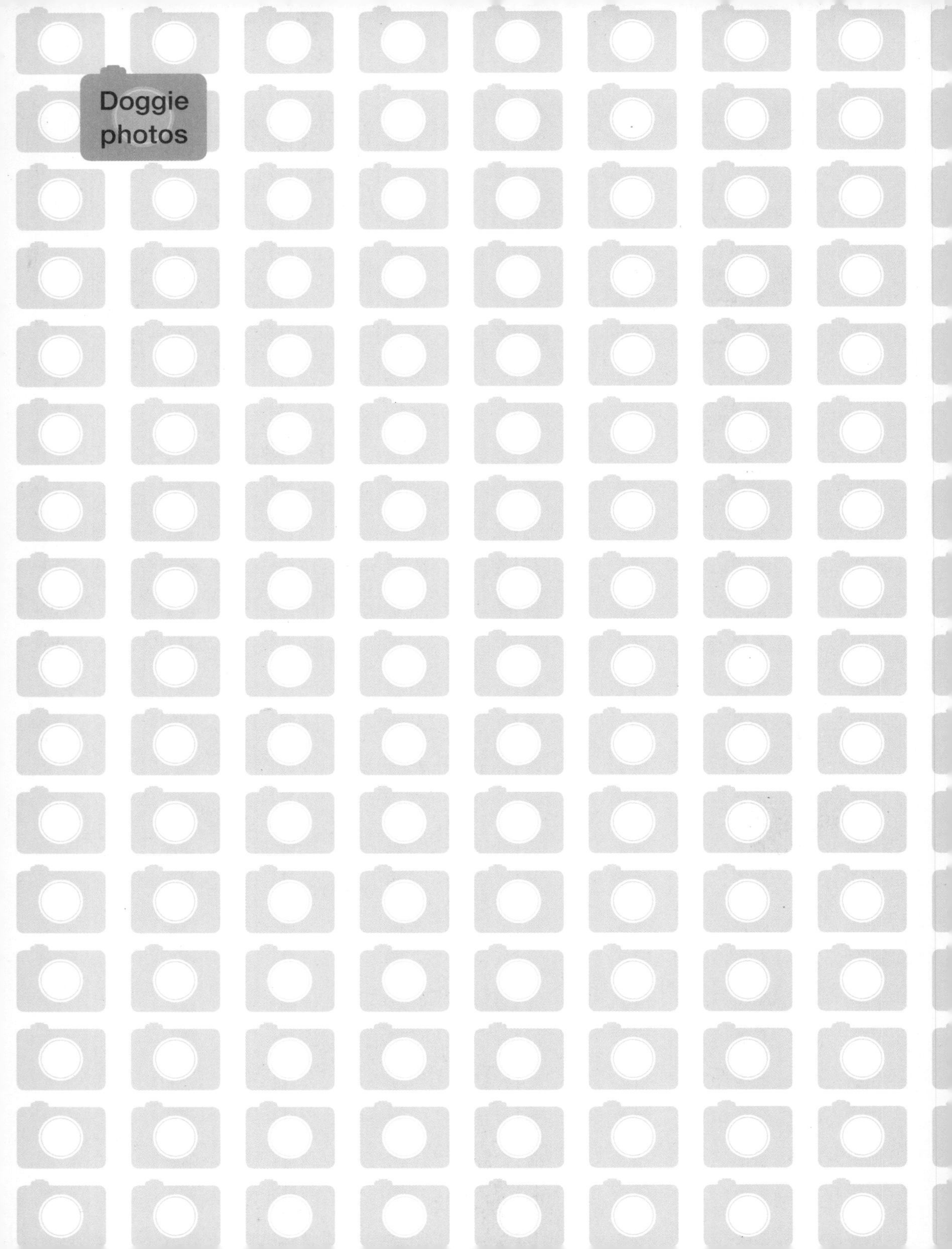
Doggie
photos